This is me

In this topic, learners are encouraged to:

- find and create patterns
- retell events and stories with help
- count objects and sounds
- hold a pencil or crayon
- identify familiar shapes.

Teachers will also help learners to:

- join in with rhyming games and activities
- talk with and listen to others
- count from 1 to 5 and use the numbers to play
- say when they're hungry, thirsty, or tired
- learn about the world around them
- use different materials to model familiar places and people.

My new school

1, 2, 3,

a Sing the Welcome song.

b Find a child who looks sad.

c Look. What is Rani doing?

d Find Tarek. Talk about the pattern he is making.

At home
What objects in the picture can you find at home? Ask your child to name them.

In these sessions, children will also: learn each other's names, explore their classroom, paint pictures of themselves, try writing their names, explore different ways of moving.
→ TG pp. 19–22

Explore

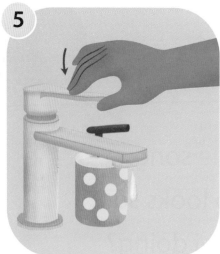

a Say what Rani is doing in each picture.

In this session, children will also: mime actions with their hands, learn about hand washing and practise it themselves, make hand prints. → TG pp. 19–22

At home

Talk about getting ready for school. Ask your child: *What do you do first?/ next?/last?*

My new school

a Choose 1 crayon. What colour is it?

b Colour the beads in a pattern.

In this session, children will also: start to name different colours, look at patterns, make their own patterns with colours and shapes. → TG pp. 19–22

At home

Use 2 or 3 colours to draw or paint a repeating pattern. Ask: *What colour comes next?*

7

My new school

Connect

a Say how Tarek feels in each picture.

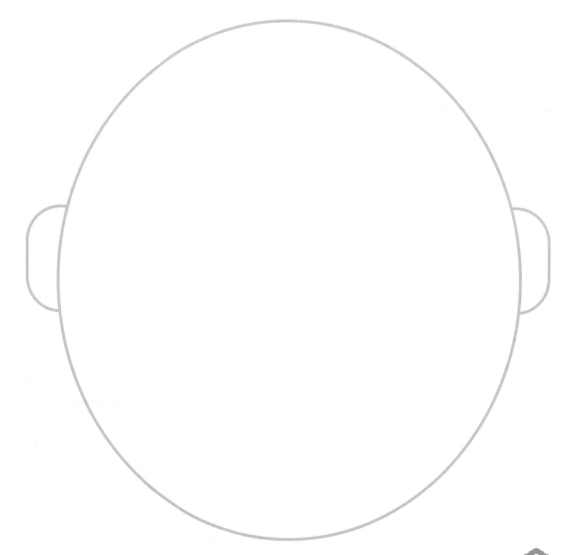

b How do you feel? Draw your face.

At home

Take turns with your child to pretend to be happy, sad, or sleepy. The other person guesses the feeling.

8

In this session, children will also: name different feelings, talk about their own feelings, attend to their toileting needs. → TG pp. 19–22

My feelings

a Count the balls.

b Look. What are the children doing?

At home

Choose 2 different-sized or different-coloured plates or bowls. Ask: *How are they the same? How are they different?*

In this session, children will also: look for similarities and differences, talk about feeling shy, write letter shapes, play snap to learn names for body parts. → TG pp. 23–25

9

My feelings

a Look. How are the children feeling?

b Listen to your teacher's descriptions and find each child.

At home

Look at pictures of families in books or photos. Ask your child questions like: *Who has brown hair? Who has blue eyes? Who has skin colour like yours?*

In this session, children will also: learn the 'Feelings' song, look at pictures and name feelings, make happy/sad stick puppets, sort items by colour. → TG pp. 23–25

My feelings

a Look. What are the children doing?

b Say. Have you felt the same? When?

At home

Talk with your child about a time when they were sad or happy. Can they remember what happened and how they felt?

In this session, children will also: talk about feelings they have had in different situations, make jigsaws, practise moving in different ways. → TG pp. 23–25

My feelings

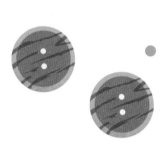

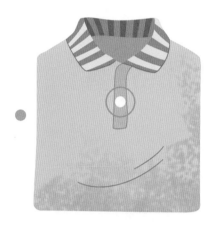

a Count each set of buttons.

b Draw lines to match the buttons with the clothes.

At home

Practise counting the buttons on your child's clothes when dressing and undressing.

In this session, children will also: talk about clothes, dress up and practise using different fastenings, count and sort into sets, sing 'If you're happy and you know it' → TG pp. 23–25

My feelings

a Look. Why are some children upset?

b Trace the lines. How do the friends help?

At home

Encourage your child to help you with household tasks, like folding clothes and putting away toys.

In this session, children will also: share a story about friendship, think about how to be a good friend, practice tracing lines, make jigsaws of faces. → TG pp. 23–25

13

My amazing body

a Chant One finger, one thumb.

b Look. What are the children doing with their arms?

c Count the children in the sand.

d What do you like to do outdoors?

At home

Play 'Mama/Papa says ...' Say: *Mama/Papa says jump up and down!* Change this to different actions.

In these sessions, children will also: make models of people and objects, do an obstacle course, hear a story about a race. → TG pp. 26–29

15

My amazing body

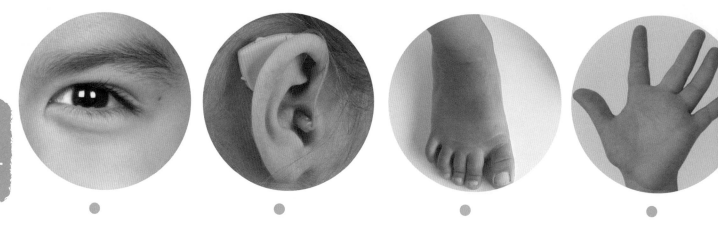

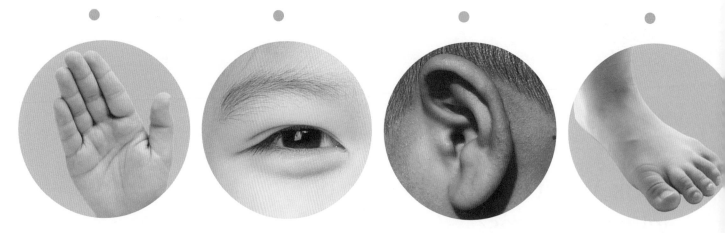

a Draw the lines to match the same body parts.

b Count the fingers.

In this session, children will also: name and match body parts, use their hands to make patterns and pick up tiny objects. → TG p. pp. 26–29

At home

Look at pictures of animals. Help your child to count their eyes, ears, nose, tail, and other parts.

My amazing body

a Look. Where are the children?

b Listen to your teacher.
Move like the children in the picture.

In this session, children will also: dance together, learn about the importance of drinking water, play 'Follow the leader', talk about how music makes them feel. → TG p. pp. 26–29

At home

Make up some new dance moves with your child. Take turns to copy what each other is doing.

My amazing body

a Find the parts of the body the children are using.

b Look at the flags. What pattern do the colours make?

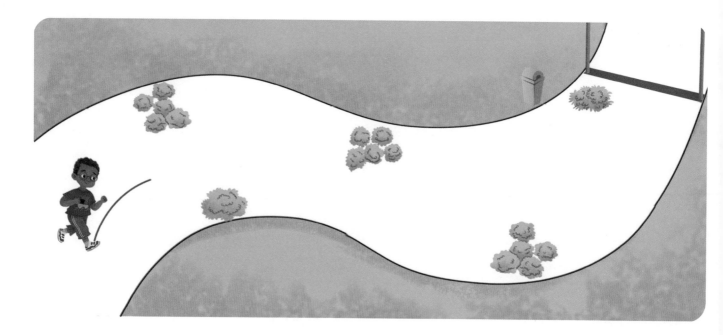

c Continue the line to help Tarek finish the race.

At home

Talk about a competition your child has been in or seen. Ask: *How do you feel when you are competing?*

In this session, children will also: review their learning by: counting to 4, naming body parts and colours, listening to a story, taking part in races. → TG pp. 26–29

My animal toys

Jen the hen

1

2

3

4

a Count. How many footprints can you see in each picture?

b Retell the story.

In this session, children will also: play 'hide and seek', practise looking closely at details, count claps and steps. → TG pp. 29–32

At home

Ask your child to hide a toy while you close your eyes. Open your eyes, look around and guess where it is. Ask: *Is it in the basket? Is it behind the sofa?*

19

My animal toys

a Draw lines to match each toy with the correct game.

b Listen to your teacher and count the toys.

In this session, children will also: talk about their favourite animal toys, pretend play, form letter shapes for labels. → TG pp. 29–32

At home

Play 'I spy with my little eye' using colours. Say: *I spy something that is green/ red/yellow/blue.* Ask your child to guess the answer.

My animal toys

Explore

a Count the horses. Count the hens.

b Look. Which animal is there most of?

At home

Draw or look at some simple pictures of animals, for example, 3 cats, 2 spiders, and 1 butterfly. Ask your child to count them.

21

In this session, children will also: learn 'Five little ducks ...'; talk about farm animals, sort and count sets of animals, recognize the number for their age. → TG pp. 29–32

My animal toys

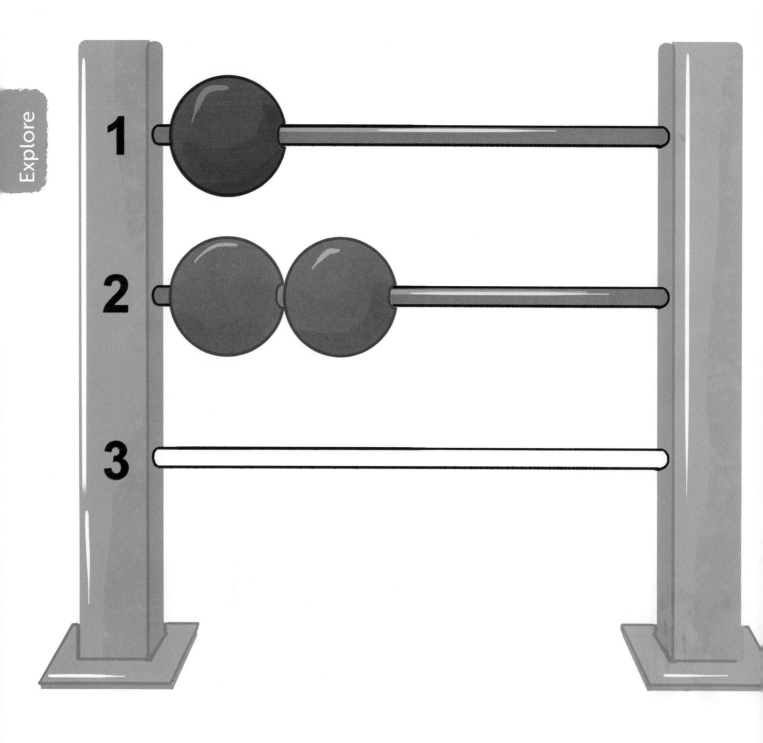

a Draw the beads for number 3.

b Put 1 toy animal on each bead.
How many toys are in each row?

In this session, children will also: practise counting up to and down from 5, count sets of objects, play 'Spot it', make model animal shelters. → TG pp. 29–32

At home

Ask your child: *How old are you? Can you find that number of books/toys/leaves?*

My animal toys

a Look. How do you play the game?

b Count the objects on each tray.

In this session, children will also: play 'I spy with my little eye' using descriptions of objects; talk about playing well together; look for numbers in the classroom and outside. → TG pp. 29–32

Connect

At home
Play the memory game using your child's favourite small toys.

My favourite sounds

a Sing I can listen.

b Look. How many sounds would you hear if you were there?

c Find a quiet sound in the picture.

d Find a loud sound in the picture.

At home
Ask your child to stop and listen for 1 minute, inside and outside. Ask: *What can you hear?*

In these sessions, children will also: compare loud and quiet sounds, go for a 'sound walk', record sounds, sing and dance. → TG pp. 33–36

a Find the fillings for the shakers.

b Count the children making a shaker.

In this session, children will also: learn how to make a shaker and make their own, shake a rhythm and count sounds, write a name label. → TG pp. 33–36

At home

Choose some everyday objects to shake. Ask: *Do they make a sound? Can you make a rhythm (sound pattern)?*

My favourite sounds

a Say each animal's name.

b Try. Can you make each animal's sound?

c Circle the animal that has 2 legs.

In this session, children will also: name familiar animals, identify their sounds, make an animal collage, share a story about animals. → TG pp. 33–36

At home
Take turns to make an animal sound. The other person guesses the animal.

27

My favourite sounds

a Say what the baby is doing.

b Look. Which actions can wake the baby?

In this session, children will also: talk about caring for a baby, sing quiet songs, play a game about being quiet. → TG pp. 33–36

At home

Talk about being quiet or loud. Ask: *When do you need to be quiet? When do you need to be loud? Why?*

My school lunch

Fussy Felix

a Look. What shapes can you see?

b Retell the story.

In this session, children will also: sing about food, explore food textures, talk about their own food likes and dislikes. → TG pp. 36–39

At home

Find some things with different smells at home. Ask your child to describe the smells.

My school lunch

a Listen to your teacher and find the shapes.

b Draw 1 shape and colour it in.

In this session, children will also: find food shapes in snacks, identify shapes in the school environment, try some snacks. → TG pp. 36–39

At home

Put 3 food items into separate plastic bowls. Cover your child's eyes. Can they guess the food by smell and touch?

My school lunch

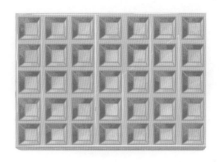

a Name the coloured shapes.

b Circle the foods using the same colour as their shape.

In this session, children will also: match colours and shapes, make shapes with their bodies, create pretend food. → TG pp. 36–39

At home

Look for 2D shapes at home, such as tiles on the floor or walls, and in curtain or rug patterns. Ask: *What is that shape called?*

31

a Count the fruits.

b Draw lines to match each piece of fruit with the whole fruit.

In this session, children will also: look at the outside and inside of fruit, taste fruit and explain why they like/dislike it, make model fruit. → TG pp. 36–39

At home

Name fruits and vegetables at home and in shops.

My school lunch

a Listen to your teacher and colour the things.

b Who is making the loudest noise?

At home

Walk around your home. Encourage your child to describe what they can hear.

33

In this session, children will: also: review their learning through familiar songs, stories, games, counting and naming shapes, using prepositions. → TG pp. 36–39

People around me!

In this topic, learners are encouraged to:

- identify family and friends in stories and in the real world
- use numbers 1 to 5
- group 5 objects into sets
- identify and express feelings
- talk about people who help the community
- hold a pencil or crayon correctly.

Teachers will also help learners to:

- talk with and listen to others
- role-play community helpers
- begin to make marks for letters and numbers
- recognize numbers significant to them
- solve simple number problems
- play in a group with other children, with support.

Families

a Look. Where is Tarek?

b Count the children.

c Find the baby.

d What are they celebrating?

In these sessions, children will also: learn a 'families' rhyme, retell a story, read and write their name, look at photos, talk about their families, make a celebration cake. → TG pp. 40–43

At home

Look at family photos with your child and help identify family members. Say: *Where is your aunt? Where are your cousins?*

Families

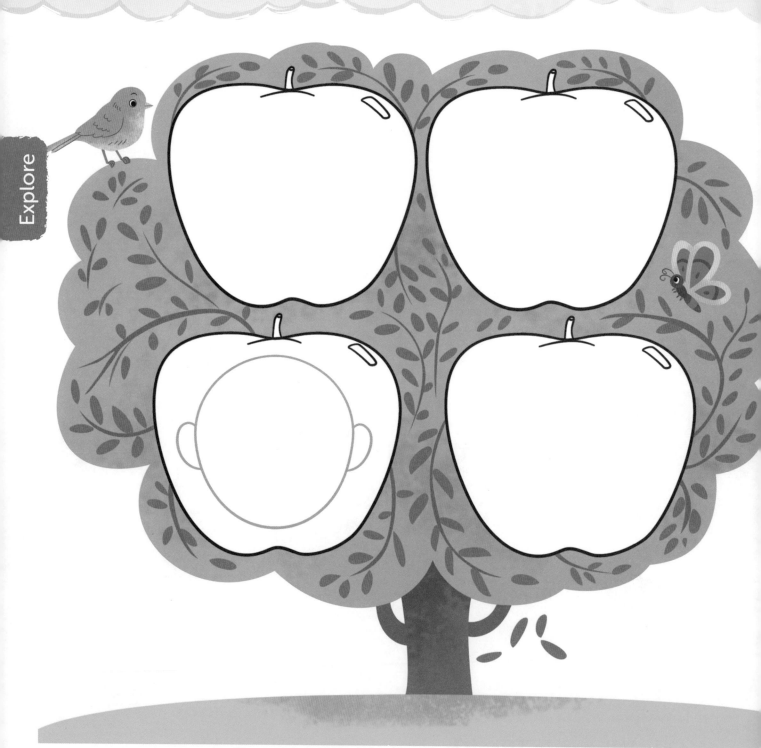

a Draw your face to complete the picture.

b Add 3 members of your family in the other apples.

In this session, children will also: look at trees, find out about family trees, make their own simple family tree, practise counting to 3. → TG pp. 40–43

At home

Make your own family tree and talk about who all the people are. Discuss some of the things your child likes to do with them.

Families

a Look. How many people are in this family?

b Listen to your teacher and count the things.

In this session, children will also: practise counting different things, hear a story about family, remember important family events, move in different ways. → TG pp. 40–43

At home

Help your child count your family members. Ask: *How many people are there in our family?*

Families

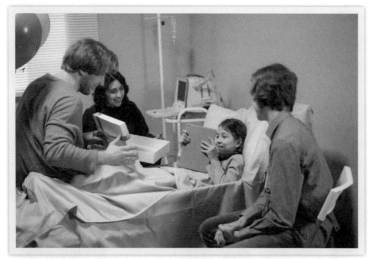

a Complete the circles to show the number of people in each family.

In this session, children will also: talk about giving presents and cards, match sets with numbers, make a card. → TG pp. 40–43

Friends

a Sing Will you be my friend today?.

b Look. What is the class doing?

c Listen to your teacher and count the things.

At home

Make arrangements with another parent/tutor for a play date.

In this session, children will also: talk about making friends, count objects, make handprints with a friend. → TG pp. 44–46

Explore

a Find the thumb on the hand.

b Count. How many fingers can you see?

c Look. Do a high five with a friend.

In this session, children will also: sing a song, talk about their friends, get dressed for a walk, go for a walk. → TG pp. 44–46

At home

Discuss your child's friends, and what they like to do together.

Friends

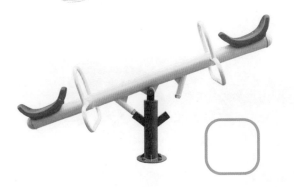

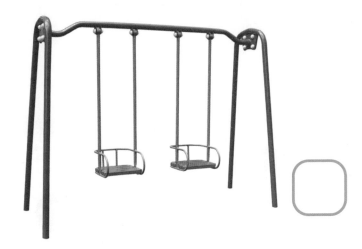

a Look. How many children can use each thing?

b Tick (✓) your favourite playground equipment.

In this session, children will also: listen to a story about friendship, play a board game, talk about taking turns. → TG pp. 44–46

Friends

Explore

a Look. How are the children feeling?

b Circle the children sharing.

At home

Show your child photos of some family members. Describe one family member and ask your child to guess who it is.

In this session, children will also: talk about feelings, practise sharing sets of 4, play 'One little elephant went out to play', read stories. → TG pp. 44–46

Friends

a Find the mums and dads.

b Tick (✓) the picture with the grandparent.

c Draw the family or friends from your favourite story.

At home

Talk about similarities and differences within families you know. For example, say: *Maya has one brother. How many do you have?*

In this session, children will also: compare their family with their friend's family, share stories about friends, make a collage picture of a friend. → TG pp. 44–46

Helpers

a Look. What is the class doing?

b Find each helper's tools.

c How do these workers help us?

d Move as you say the Three little fire engines rhyme.

At home

Talk with your child about one community helper they know. What do they do? Do they wear a uniform? Why is their job important?

In these sessions, children will also: dress up and role-play, count as part of play, find out about helpers' jobs, make up questions for a visitor. → TG pp. 47–49

Explore

a Find the computer and the rabbit.

b Listen to your teacher and answer. Who are the helpers?

At home

Take turns to act out doing different types of work, such as building a wall, driving a bus, or being a lifeguard. Talk about what you are doing.

In this session, children will also: create pictures and write labels, practise counting to 5, listen to a visitor talk about their job and ask questions. → TG pp. 47–49

Helpers

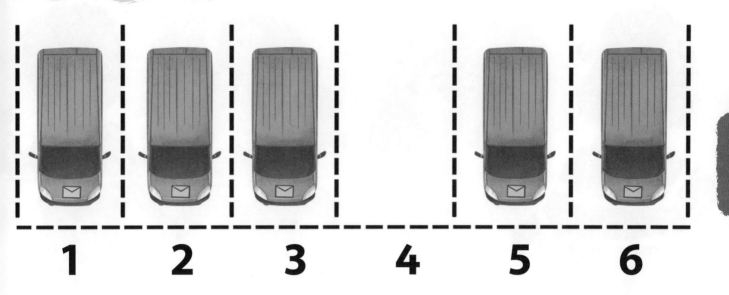

1   2   3   4   5   6

a Count the vans.

b Draw 5 vans in the empty car park.

In this session, children will also: match vehicles to helpers, separate a group of objects in different ways, play in a pretend post office, write letters and wrap up parcels. → TG pp. 47–49

Explore

At home
Give your child a set of 5 objects. How many different ways can they split them into 2 groups? (1 and 4, 2 and 3, 3 and 2, 4 and 1.)

47

Helpers

a Colour the things on the shelf.

b Draw lines to match the jobs with the things.

c Tick (✓) your favourite helper.

In this session, children will also: review community workers in a guessing game, draw and talk about someone important to them, review numbers 1–5. → TG pp. 47–49

At home

Talk about people who help your family and what they do. How many different helpers can your child think of?

Healthy, happy me!

In this topic, learners are encouraged to:

- explore foods and talk about feeling hungry
- identify being active with well-being
- express their feelings and identify others' feelings
- explore ways to calm down
- group 5 items differently understanding that the total is the same.

Teachers will also help learners to:

- join in with songs and rhymes
- learn about the world around them
- share and retell simple stories
- begin to make simple labels
- talk with and listen to others
- make models with different materials.

Eating healthy food

a Look. Which toppings have you tried with your yogurt?

b Count the bowls on the table.

c Find Fiona. Why is her tummy hurting?

At home

Encourage your child to try a new type of fruit or vegetable. Ask: *What does it taste like? Do you like it? Why?*

In these sessions, children will also: discuss food choices, review handwashing, talk about feeling hungry and full, try new foods, recognize familiar words and logos. → TG pp. 50–53

Eating healthy food

a Follow the lines. Name the pizza toppings.

b Circle the toppings you would put on your pizza.

In this session, children will also: find out about pizza toppings, talk about likes and dislikes, explore 'more' and 'less' by sharing pizza pieces. → TG pp. 50–53

At home

Talk about different types of food. Ask your child to sort them into food they like and food they don't like.

Eating healthy food

a Tick (✓) the healthy foods.

b Which foods would you eat only for a treat?

c How many foods are there in each group?

At home

Compare 2 sets of items at home, for example, when setting the table give your child 3 forks and 2 spoons. Ask: *Which group has more?*

53

Eating healthy food

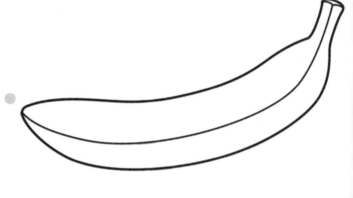
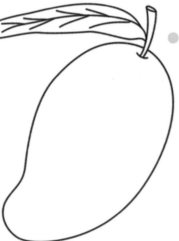

a Draw lines to match the pictures with the fruits.

b Colour the fruits.

At home

Cut up some different fruits and place each in separate bowls. Blindfold your child. Ask them to identify the fruit through touch, smell, and (finally) taste.

54

In this session, children will also: find out how fruit grows, learn about fruit growing locally, plant and tend a seed, play a counting game. → TG pp. 50–53

Being active

The race

a Look. What is Tarek doing in each picture?

b Retell the story.

In this session, children will also: act out the story, do warm up exercises, count movements.
→ TG pp. 54–56

At home

Make some movements and ask your child to copy them (for example, hop, skip, run, twirl, crawl).

55

Being active

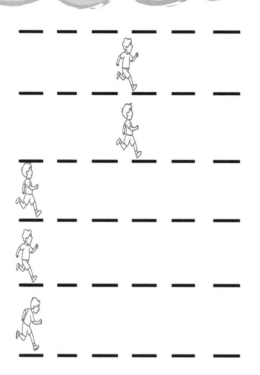
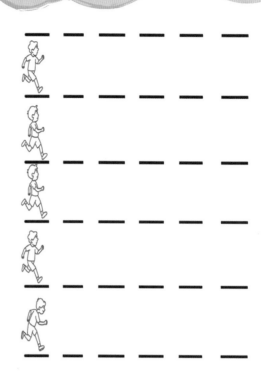

a Count the runners on each track.

— — — — — — — — — —

— — — — — — — — — —

— — — — — — — — —

— — — — — — — —

— — — — — — — —

— — — — — — — —

b Draw 5 runners in 2 groups.

In this session, children will also: help plan and then take part in races, try different ways of dividing 5, make a model person with moving legs. → TG pp. 54–56

At home

Explore different ways to make 5, using everyday objects, such as buttons in 2 bowls. Keep changing the arrangement, but show the total is still 5.

Being active

a Look. Show the child sliding down.

b Count the children climbing.

c Say the Here are my legs rhyme.

In this session, children will also: practise climbing, jump on mats with different shapes.
→ TG pp. 54–56

At home

Use words to describe position. Say: *Can you put the ball <u>in</u> the bag? Is the dog <u>under</u> the table?*

a Tick (✓) the things you know.
Count them.

b Mime how you would use them.

In this session, children will also: talk about sports equipment and exercise, draw and label a picture of their favourite exercise, learn about 'more' and 'less'. → TG pp. 54–56

At home

Choose a physical exercise or game that the whole family can do. Encourage your child to 'teach' everyone how to play.

Being active

a Name the animals.

b Move like a kangaroo. Move like a snail.

c Colour the parts of the bird and kangaroo that help them move.

At home

Take turns with your child to move like an animal. Can the other person guess the animal?

In this session, children will also: find out about animal movements, try moving like different animals, make models of animals. → TG pp. 54–56

Staying calm

a Look. What are the children doing?

b Find a child that looks upset.

c Sit like Gibran. Breathe in and out.

d Say the Calming down rhyme.

At home

Talk with your child about ways of calming down when they feel upset. Can they think of a few different things that can help?

In these sessions, children will also: talk about emotions and feeling calm, listen to stories about emotions, share favourite books, make signs for the calm corner. → TG pp. 57–59

Staying calm

a Listen to your teacher and play Stepping stones.

b Count the bushes and the flowers.

In this session, children will also: practise being calm outside, look at details in the natural environment, listen to calm music while they paint. → TG pp. 57–59

At home

Play games that involve counting like snakes and ladders or dominoes with spots. Encourage your child to be considerate whether they win or lose.

Staying calm

a Find the leaves in the picture.

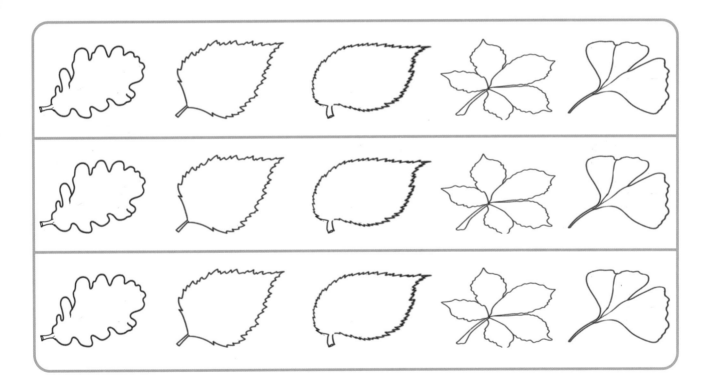

b Use 2 colours to colour each line of leaves.

c Count the leaves in each line.

In this session, children will also: make patterns with natural objects, count down from 5 to 0, make a den. → TG pp. 57–59

At home

Enjoy some relaxing time outside with your child. Use natural objects for counting and making patterns.

Staying calm

a Draw lines to match the pictures.
How many pairs do you have?

b Count the girls and boys in the pictures.

c Listen to your teacher and find
the children.

At home

Talk about healthy
habits with your child.
Can they think of some
healthy ways to snack, keep
fit and relax?

In this session, children will also: review things that help them be happy and healthy, choose
healthy snacks, dance to music, practise breathing slowly. → TG pp. 57–59